Violin Exam Pieces

ABRSM Grade 3

Selected from the 2020–2023 syllabus

Name

C000292363

Date of exam

Contents

Violin consultant: Kathy Blackwell
Footnotes: Anthony Burton

Other pieces for Grade 3   DUET *with violin accompaniment*   PF/VN *with piano or violin accompaniment*

LIST A

4   **Boyce**   Gavotte (3rd movt from *Symphony No. 4 in F*, Op. 2 No. 4), arr. Wade. *The Young Symphonist, Vol. 2* (Spartan Press)

5   **Holmstad**   Lett på fot (Light-footed) (*with 1st repeat*). Holmstad: *Gamle danser blir som nye* (Norsk Musikforlag) SOLO

6   **Kling**   March, arr. Gazda & Clark (*upper part*). *Compatible Duets for Strings, Vol. 2: Violin* (Carl Fischer) DUET

7   **F. Küchler**   Allegro assai: 3rd movt from *Concertino in D*, Op. 15 (Bosworth)

8   **Mascitti**   Gavotta (4th movt from *Sonata in E minor*, Op. 2 No. 10). *Baroque Violin Pieces, Book 1* (ABRSM)

9   **Mozart**   Duo (from *12 Duos*, K. 487), arr. de Keyser & Waterman (*upper part*). *The Young Violinist's Repertoire, Book 3* (Faber) DUET

10   **Telemann**   Bourrée (from *Wedding Divertissement*). *The Best of Grade 3 Violin* (Faber)

LIST B

4   **Bizet**   Habanera (from *Carmen*), arr. K. & D. Blackwell. *Fiddle Time Sprinters* (OUP) PF/VN

5   **G. Concone**   Andante pastorale, arr. Gazda & Clark (*upper part*). *Compatible Duets for Strings, Vol. 2: Violin* (Carl Fischer) DUET

6   **Gebirtig**   Moishele Mayn Fraynd, arr. Rowlands. *Klezmer Fiddle Tunes* (Schott)

7   **Barbara Heller**   Lalai – A Lullaby to Awaken You?, arr. Mohrs. *My First Concert for Violin* (Schott)

8   **Elton John & Tim Rice**   Can You Feel the Love Tonight? (from *The Lion King*), arr. Galliford & Neuburg. *Top Hits from TV, Movies & Musicals for Violin* (Alfred)

9   **Papini**   Theme *and* Variations 1 *and* 2 (from *Theme and Variations*), trans. Applebaum. *Solos for Young Violinists, Vol. 1* (Alfred)

10   **Friedrich Seitz**   Adagio: 2nd movt from *Student Concerto No. 2 in G*, Op. 13 (Bärenreiter)

LIST C

4   **Bartók**   Pillow Dance: No. 14 from *44 Duos for Two Violins, Vol. 1* (*upper part*) (Universal) DUET

5   **L. Bernstein**   I feel pretty (from *West Side Story*), arr. Wastall (*solo part*). *Session Time for Strings: Violin* (Boosey & Hawkes)

6   **Katherine & Hugh Colledge**   Stiffkey Blues: No. 21 from *Shooting Stars for Violin* (Boosey & Hawkes)

7   **C. Dancla**   Chasse du jeune Henry: No. 17 from *36 études mélodiques et faciles*, Op. 84 (Schott) SOLO

8   **Grechaninov**   The Joker (No. 3 from *Early Morning*, Op. 126a). *The Young Violinist's Repertoire, Book 3* (Faber)

9   **Thomas Gregory**   Vamoose. *Vamoosh Violin, Book 2* (Vamoosh)

10   **Sheila Nelson**   Toad in the Hole (*upper part; without improvisation*). *Technitunes for Violin* (Boosey & Hawkes) PF/VN

First published in 2019 by ABRSM (Publishing) Ltd,
a wholly owned subsidiary of ABRSM, 4 London Wall Place,
London EC2Y 5AU, United Kingdom
© 2019 by The Associated Board of the Royal Schools of Music
Distributed worldwide by Oxford University Press

Music origination by Julia Bovee
Cover by Kate Benjamin & Andy Potts, with thanks to Brighton College
Printed in England by Halstan & Co. Ltd, Amersham, Bucks.,
on materials from sustainable sources.
P15146

Rejoicing

La réjouissance

Fourth movement from *Music for the Royal Fireworks*, HWV 351

Arranged by ABRSM

G. F. Handel
(1685–1759)

George Frideric Handel was born in Germany, but spent the last 47 years of his life in England, where he became famous as a composer of operas, oratorios and instrumental music. In 1749, he wrote his *Music for the Royal Fireworks* to accompany a firework display in Green Park in London celebrating the end of a European war. It was played by a band of about 100 musicians: oboes, bassoons, horns, trumpets and drums, and probably strings as well, in defiance of King George II's reported remarks that he wanted 'martial music' and 'hoped there would be no fiddles'.

Theme and Variation

from Symphony No. 94, Hob. I:94, second movement

A:2

Arranged by James Alexander
and Barrie Carson Turner

Joseph Haydn
(1732–1809)

The Austrian composer Joseph Haydn made two extended visits to London in the 1790s. During his stay he directed the first performances of the last 12 of his more than 100 orchestral symphonies. The Symphony No. 94, first performed in March 1792, is known in English-speaking countries as the 'Surprise' Symphony, because the theme of the second movement is interrupted at one point (on the second beat of bar 8, in the repeat) by a sudden, startling loud chord for the full orchestra. This free arrangement presents the theme, *without* the surprise, followed by a version of the final variation of the movement.

Contredanse

No. 1 from 12 contredanses, K. 269b

Transcribed and edited
by Richard Jones

attrib. W. A. Mozart
(1756–91)

The contredanse was a popular 18th-century dance in lively two-in-a-bar metre, which began its life in France as a version of the English 'country dance'. (Its name is a French pronunciation of the English term.) This example comes from a set of contredanses said to have been written by the Austrian composer Wolfgang Amadeus Mozart, probably in 1776 or 1777, for a local nobleman in his home town of Salzburg. The set was originally for orchestra, but all that has survived of it is a group of four dances in an arrangement for solo piano. It is now thought unlikely that Mozart wrote these.

B:1

Theme from Berceuse

from *Dolly*, Op. 56

Arranged by David Blackwell

Gabriel Fauré
(1845–1924)

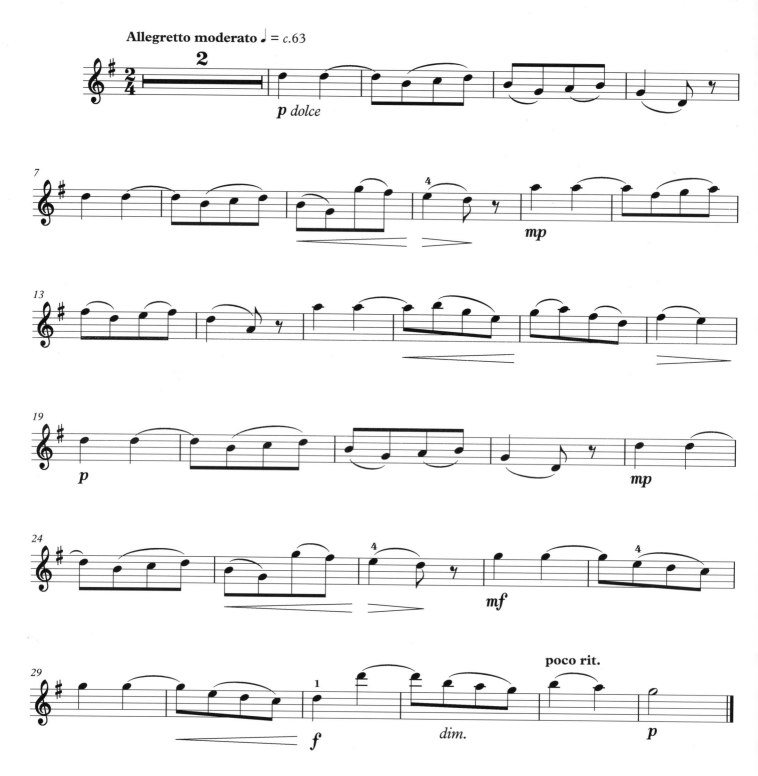

The French composer Gabriel Fauré wrote his suite *Dolly* for piano duet (four hands on one keyboard) in the mid-1890s for Dolly, the young daughter of his friend Emma Bardac. He sent the first movement, 'Berceuse', to Dolly in June 1893 for her first birthday; it was an adaptation of a piece he had written nearly 30 years earlier. The title means 'Cradle song': you can hear the rocking of the cradle in the repeated figures of the piano accompaniment to the smooth melody. The piece is often remembered as the music for the BBC radio series *Listen with Mother*, which ran from 1950 to 1982.

Little Boy of Bachín

Chiquilín de Bachín

B:2

Arranged by Edward Huws Jones

Music by Astor Piazzolla (1921-92)
Lyrics by Horacio Ferrer (1933-2014)

The Argentine musician Astor Piazzolla was a leading figure, as a band-leader, composer and player of the bandoneon (button accordion), in the development of the tango, his country's national dance. This piece, however, is not a tango, but a popular song in slow waltz time. First released in 1969, it has words by a frequent collaborator with Piazzolla, the Uruguayan-Argentine poet Horacio Ferrer. They describe a poor young boy selling flowers in the Bachín restaurant in the theatre district of the Argentine capital Buenos Aires. The boy was a real person: he was eleven at the time the song was written, and when it was finished Piazzolla and Ferrer performed it to him in his family's one-room apartment.

Andante

Second movement from Concerto in B minor, Op. 35

Oskar Rieding
(1840–1916)

Oskar Rieding was born in north Germany, studied in Berlin and Leipzig, and worked as an orchestral violinist in Vienna. But he spent most of his career in the Hungarian capital, Budapest, where he was leader of the Opera orchestra from 1871 to 1904. After that, he retired to Cilli (Celje), then in Hungary but now in Slovenia. Rieding wrote many educational works for violin with piano. Some of the best known are in the form of the Romantic concerto – including the Concerto in B minor, first published in 1909, of which this is the central slow movement.

Source: *Violin Concerto in B minor, Op. 35* (Leipzig: Bosworth & Co., 1909).

Singin' in the Rain

Arranged by Nikki Iles

Music by N. H. Brown (1896–1964)
Lyrics by Arthur Freed (1894–1973)

'Singin' in the Rain' is a song with words by Arthur Freed and music by Nacio Herb Brown, probably first performed in the film *The Hollywood Revue* of 1929. It became well known through its use in the 1952 film which took its name, set in the late 1920s when silent films were giving way to 'talking pictures'. In that, it was a song-and-dance number for Gene Kelly, cheerfully splashing his way through heavy rain and deep puddles. This arrangement is by the British jazz pianist and educator Nikki Iles.

Shadow Wizard

Rachel Stott
(born 1968)

Rachel Stott is a composer, violist and teacher based in London. She says about this piece, specially written for ABRSM: 'Shadow Wizard was inspired by the fantasy novel *A Wizard of Earthsea* by Ursula K. Le Guin. Written years before the Harry Potter books, it is the story of an orphaned boy, Ged, who goes to a school for wizardry and does battle with the dark forces of evil. The 'shadow' which pursues Ged throughout the book is finally vanquished when he addresses it by his own name. The *sul tasto* effect at the end of the piece should suggest the disappearing of the evil shadow; *sul tasto estremo* – playing with the bow a long way over the fingerboard – produces a sound like blowing over a milk bottle.'

Relaxing in Rio

No. 3 from *Violin Globetrotters*

Ros Stephen
(born 1972)

Ros Stephen is a violinist, composer and arranger based in London. She describes her *Globetrotters* series as a collection of pieces intended to be 'technically accessible, fun to play, and an introduction to different styles of music from around the world'. This piece takes us to Brazil, and to the seaside city of Rio de Janeiro, where in the late 1950s young musicians formulated the style called 'bossa nova' (new wave), with its subtle syncopated rhythm.